MW EDUCATIONAL

THE A PLUS SERIES OF 11+ PRACTICE PAPERS

ENGLISH

Volume 1 Multiple Choice Format

INSTRUCTIONS FOR THE PERSON TAKING THE TESTS

Please read these instructions before you start the English tests

1. Do not begin any of the tests until you are instructed to do so. You will be allowed 45 minutes to do each test.

2. Try and answer as many questions as you can. If you find that you cannot answer a question, do not waste time trying to answer it. Leave that question and come back to it at the end if you have any time left.

3. This is a multiple-choice test. You should mark your answers on the answer sheet provided at the end of this booklet and not on the test paper.

4. To answer a question, draw a line <u>in pencil</u> across the box that is <u>next</u> to the correct answer. If you wish to change an answer, simply rub out your line and draw a fresh line in another box. Some examples have been done to help you.

5. Work as quickly as you can, taking care that you do not miss any questions out.

6. If you complete a test before the end of the allotted time, go back over your test, checking that you have not missed out any questions and check your answers

7. Once the test has begun, you are not allowed to ask any questions.

© MW Educational/Hadleigh Books 2017

PAPER 1

Read through the following passage, then answer the questions beneath it, by choosing the correct letter - a, b, c or d – and marking this choice on the answer sheet provided. The passage is about how a house is built.

Building a house is not a simple affair, but one that involves several different stages, with input from several types of tradesmen. First of all before the building work is started, the builder must apply for planning permission to build on the piece of land he has bought, which is called a "plot". Plans of what the house is going to look like must also be drawn up by an architect. The
5   local council will then give planning permission for the house building to go ahead. Once the site has been cleared of all vegetation and debris, measurements are taken following the plans. Then the foundations are dug. These are trenches about a metre in depth into which concrete is poured. Once this has set, bricklayers can start building the outside and inner walls of the house on top of these. From time to time the local council will send in an inspector to check that certain
10   building regulations are being followed. Many houses now use breezeblocks instead of bricks on some of the inner walls. These are much bigger than bricks and save on costs. They make the job quicker and easier. Once the ground floor walls have been built, beams are put across the top of them so that a ceiling and floor can be put in for the next story (or level). The walls are then built up until they are high enough for the roof beams to be added.
15   At the same time joiners, electricians and plumbers are working down below making sure that the house has electricity, water and floorboards. In many areas gas pipes might also be installed along with central heating. Once the roof beams are in position, roofers move in to lay down felt and then place tiles on the roof to make the house watertight. Finally glaziers put in the windows so that the house is now ready to be decorated. On the outside, fences will be built so that the garden is separated from the house next door. Soon the house is ready for someone to move into it.

1)   "Tradesmen" (line 2) are: -
(a) architects   (b) councillors   (c) workmen   (d) inspectors

2)   A "plot" (line 4) is a: -
(a) a trench   (b) a piece of land   (c) a plan   (d) a crime

3)   What do you think "debris" (line 6) is?
(a) bricks   (b) rubbish   (c) trees   (d) soil

4)   Another word for "regulations" (line 10) would be: -
(a) buildings   (b) architects   (c) foundations   (d) rules

5)   How do breezeblocks make the job "quicker and easier"?
(a)   They are tougher than brick
(b)   They are smaller than bricks
(c)   They are softer than bricks
(d)   They take up more room than bricks

6)   What do you think a joiner would put into the house?
(a) electricity   (b) gas pipes   (c) floor boards   (d) water pipes

7) "Watertight" (line 18) means:-
   (a)   Water is kept in the roof   (b)   Rain water can't get into the rest of the house
   (c)   Rain water goes down to the drains   (d)   Water is put into water pipes

8) If someone "decorates" the house (line 19), it means that he or she: -
   (a)   Puts wallpaper on the walls   (b)   Puts central heating in
   (c)   Puts electricity into the house   (d)   Puts fences in the garden

**In the following sentences one of the following types of punctuation has been missed out: -
full stop (.) question mark (?) exclamation mark (!) inverted commas ("")
Work out what it is that is missing and then put a line against the correct sign on the answer sheet.**
An example has been done for you.

E.g.   *Where is your homework ? asked the teacher.*   ANSWER: " "

9)   Susan didn't agree with what her mother said
10) "Get a move on" shouted the officer to the soldiers.
11) "How do I get to Trafalgar Square" asked the tourist.
12) I was sorry that I missed seeing the football match
13) How are you today? enquired the old man.
14) Michael enjoyed reading The Wind In The Willows.
15) "We must leave now," said the lady "It's getting late".
16) "Are you sure it will stay dry" asked my sister.
17) "Wake up" shouted the teacher to the inattentive boy.
18) Steven said, What is on the TV tonight?

**All the words below end in either *able* or *ible*. Work out which is the correct ending and mark
your answer on the answer sheet.** *An example has been done for you.*

E.g.   *Access*   ANSWER: (access) ible

19)   Horr
20)   Comfort
21)   Imposs
22)   Digest
23)   Navig
24)   Sale
25)   Present
26)   Invinc
27)   Excit
28)   Indestruct

Read through the passage below, which is about some sea creatures called Throoples who are taken from their island home by a naturalist. Then answer the questions by choosing the correct letter - a b c or d – and marking it on the answer sheet provided.

Grandpa Throople had woken early that morning as he usually did. He'd come up to the surface of the sea and had peered around him.

He thought to himself, "Another glorious day - no more rain and thunderstorms, like last week!" But then something strange made him lie up very still and listen intently. He could
5   hear a constant loud banging noise, which seemed to be getting louder. Occasionally, there was the sound of a parrot squawking but the noise was definitely getting louder.

Suddenly, before he had time to think, everywhere went dark - not just dark, but pitch black. He could feel himself moving upwards at an incredible speed, but he couldn't move himself. Then, just as quickly, it was light again, but too light for him to see. He instinctively scurried
10   for shelter and darkness; but there was no rock for him to hide behind; no sea to cover him and no sand for him to hide in.

"A fine specimen!" boomed out a loud voice that made him shake with fear. "I don't know what it is," the voice continued, "but there are several more of them down there. Get the net ready."

"Yes Sir!" replied the voice's companion.
15   Before Grandfather Throople could realise what was happening, he was joined by Mother Throople, with Baby George; Jane Throople, Grandma Throople, Father Throople and last of all, Tom Throople; who was wriggling like anything.

If you could hear the Throoples, you would have heard ear-piercing screams coming from the tank that they were in.
20   "I can't breathe!" Jane Throople was shrieking at the top of her voice.

"My tail! Oh my tail!" screamed Grandma Throople.

Suddenly, "Whoosh", the whole Throople clan were covered in sea water. "Ah, that's better", said Grandma Throople. "But where are we?" asked Mother Throople.

"We're trapped!" replied Tom Throople.
25   "It's like we are in a box - with no way out," said Father Throople.

29)   Grandpa Throople listened "intently" (line 4). What does this mean?
    (a)   softly   (b)   with great concentration
    (c)   with very little effort   (d)   half-heartedly

30)   What do you think the noise "getting louder" was (line 6)?
    (a)   a thunderstorm   (b)   an animal coming towards the pool
    (c)   the naturalist getting closer (d)   the wind coming up

31)   "Scurried" (line 9) is what sort of movement?
    (a)   trotting slowly   (b)   galloping fast
    (c)   hopping quickly   (d)   stepping quickly

32)   In the passage what do you think a "specimen" is (line 12)?
    (a)   a small plant or animal   (b)   a stone from the sea
    (c)   a piece of seaweed   (d)   a piece of fruit

33)   How many Throoples were there altogether?
    (a)   six   (b)   seven   (c)   eight   (d)   nine

34) What is the meaning of "shrieking" (line 20)?
    (a)   screaming   (b)   laughing
    (c)   crying   (d)   whispering

35) How many humans are there in the passage?
    (a) one   (b) two   (c) three   (d) four

In the lines below, rearrange the words so that they are in alphabetical order and then work out which word would be <u>third</u> in the new order. Mark your choice on the answer sheet.

36)   water warden walrus wander waist

37)   mathematics marriage manor majestic mayor

38)   injure institute injustice indeed injury

39)   yearn yacht yarn young yesterday

40)   office offend offence official offer

41)   article arthritis armoury argument articulate

42)   particle pardon particular party parliament

43)   hotel holiday hospital holdall hostess

44)   creative crying creation cradle creamery

45)   united university uniform unity unicorn

In the following sentences there are two words in brackets that sound the same, but which are spelt differently. Work out which of the two words you think is correct for the sentence. Mark your choice on the answer sheet. *An example has been done for you.*

E.g.   *We had a lovely walk along the (peer, pier).*   *ANSWER:*   *pier*

46)   My mum had to (sew, sow) a button on my blazer.

47)   The company opened an iron (oar, ore) mine last year.

48)   The angry player (threw, through) the ball into the crowd.

49)   In the Middle Ages people ate all sorts of wild (fowl, foul).

50)   (There, Their) new school was not as nice as the old one.

51)   We soon got (bored, board) with the game we were playing.

52)   The forest was full of (beach, beech) trees.

53)   A (current, currant) is really a dried grape.

54)   I wondered (wear, where) the toilets were.

55)   The politician (made, maid) a very convincing speech.

END OF TEST PAPER ONE
CHECK THROUGH YOUR PAPER FOR ANY MISTAKES AND OMISSIONS

PAPER 2

Read the passage below and then answer the questions on it, marking the correct choice of letter in the box provided. The passage is about a visit to a hospital accident and emergency department.

As Callum struggled to get out of the car, he saw an ambulance rushing past with its sirens blaring out a monotonous wailing alarm. He held onto the roof of the car as he tried to take the weight off his right leg, which was aching with a dull pain.

His thoughts went back to the events of barely half an hour ago. He had been playing in a
5 football match for his school team, Hillbury Juniors against their local rivals: - Sunnydale. He remembered dribbling the ball through the centre of midfield and then passing it forwards to Tom Bush on the left wing. Callum continued running towards the goal and as Tom centred the ball, he stretched out to connect with it just inside the right goal post. His left foot managed to push the ball into the net but his right leg came crashing into the goal post and as a
10 result Callum was about to pay a visit to the Casualty Department of his local hospital.

A large sign said "reception" just inside the door and that is where Callum and his Dad went. After giving the details to the receptionist, Callum was shown to a cubicle where he was told that a nurse would soon see him. After an agonising wait of about ten minutes a male nurse came into the cubicle and asked Callum what he had done.
15 "Point to where it hurts", he said, but as Callum stretched, it only made the pain worse. The nurse touched the place where Callum had pointed to and gently pushed against his leg.
"Owww!" yelled Callum.
"I think that's well and truly broken", said the nurse. "But you're going to have to go down to x-ray to have some pictures taken, so that we can be absolutely sure".
20 After waiting for about another thirty minutes, a man arrived with a wheelchair and guided Callum into it. As he wheeled Callum down the corridor he whistled loudly which irritated Callum greatly. At the X-ray department another nurse asked him to lie in different positions on a table whilst she arranged the camera to take shots of his leg from different angles. "That'll do", she said once she had finished. "The x-rays will be sent back to casualty once they're ready".
25 With that Callum was whisked back to his cubicle where he was soon seen by a doctor in a white coat who asked Callum to tell him how he had broken his leg. He showed Callum one of the x-rays so he could see exactly where the fracture was but this made Callum feel a little queasy. "You'll have the leg set in plaster and then we'll let Nature take it's course", said the doctor and with that he was gone.
30 The whistling man then took Callum to another section of the hospital where a lady nurse washed his leg before putting the plaster on. "You'll feel like itching it, but you won't be able to for several weeks I'm afraid". When she was finished, Callum was told to come back in three weeks, but if there were any problems to go and see his local doctor. So after approximately three hours he was allowed to go home and start thinking about how difficult it would be to do things that he
35 had always taken for granted.

1) What do you think the word "monotonous" (line 2) means?
(a) Very loud   (b) Boring   (c) Wailing   (d) Sounding the same

2) The name of the Callum's school was: -
(a) Sunnydale   (b) Casualty   (c) Hillbury   (d) Bush

3) "Reception" (line 11) is where: -
(a) The doctor sees the patients   (b) The patients are x-rayed
(c) Broken legs are set   (d) The patient gives his name and address

4)   Why did Callum yell "Owww!"?
     (a) The nurse touched the broken bone   (b) He banged his leg on the floor
     (c) He dropped something on his leg   (d) He stretched his leg too much

5)   What was it that irritated Callum?
     (a) Having his leg x-rayed   (b) Having to wait for so long
     (c) The man whistling   (d) The pain in his leg

6)   What does "queasy" (line 27) mean?
     (a) Happy   (b) Sick   (c) Worried   (d) Energetic

7)   "Approximately" (line 33) means: -
     (a) Just about   (b) Nearly   (c) More than   (d) Nowhere near

Apostrophes are used to replace letters or words so that two words are made into one word.   In the sentences below, shorten the two words underlined so that they are joined by an apostrophe. Mark your answer on the answer sheet. *An example has been done for you.*

E.g.   *We will* be going to the market   *ANSWER:* *We'll*

8)   "Hurry up or you will be late!"
9)   I do not know what to do.
10) You must not do that !
11) I thought that he had caught a very large fish.
12) "She must have got lost," said the policeman.
13) "We can not go out today," said the teacher.
14) "You should not have done that!" shouted the man.
15) He asked me where I had got it from.
16) "Could not we go to the pictures today?".
17) You are a very naughty boy!" said the teacher.

Nouns are the names of people, places or things. Find <u>two</u> nouns in each of the sentences below. Mark your answers on the answer sheet

18)   He fell off the ladder and broke his ankle
19)   Shut the door before you leave the room.
20)   Liverpool beat Chelsea 4 - 1.
21)   The old man had a very nasty cough.
22)   Last week we could not leave the house.
23)   The raging river was moving many huge boulders.
24)   Every day I hope that the weather will be sunny.
25)   "Why don't we visit the old castle?" suggested Dad.
26)   Each morning a loud banging could be heard.
27)   "Where is the airport?" asked the visitor.

Read the passage below, which is about the hobby of train spotting and then answer the questions that are based on the passage. Mark your answers on the answer sheet provided.

Many people today scoff at the notion of train spotting. It conjures up a picture in their minds of balding, middle-aged men in anoraks on station platforms scribbling down numbers in tattered notebooks. Yet train spotting is a hobby that is popular with all members of the family – not just the males, but also the females.

5 Most people who go train spotting say it is not just the notion of managing to "spot" or "cop" a number on the side of a train that makes it worthwhile, but also the camaraderie of Train Spotters - that is the friendships that are made amongst people who share the same interest as you. Although it can be a cold and lonely hobby, especially if you are stuck on the end of a platform in January or February, waiting for the 8.47 from London to arrive,

10 it can also be a rewarding one.
In the Spring or Summer when the sun is shining, it can be very peasant in the fresh air. The older Train Spotters will no doubt tell you that train spotting today is not half as good as it was say forty or fifty years ago. That was in the age of steam when there were many more locomotives on Britain's railways, the majority of them being steam engines.

15 Whilst there may no longer be steam engines on the railway lines of Britain, (they were replaced by diesel and electric locomotives in the 1950's and 60's), there are still plenty of train spotters on Britain's railway stations, proving that train spotting is still as popular as it ever was.

28)   "Scoff" (line 1) means: -
       (a)   you are puzzled   (b)   you laugh at
       (c)   you are shocked   (d)   you are interested

29)   An "anorak" (line 2) is: -
       (a)   a type of scarf   (b)   a type of hat
       (c)   a type of shirt   (d)   a type of coat

30)   Where do most train spotters practise their hobby?
       (a)   on trains   (b)   at home
       (c)   on railway stations   (d)   on locomotives

31)   "Camaraderie" (line 6) refers to what amongst train spotters: -
       (a)   friendship   (b)   mockery
       (c)   hatred   (d)   interest

32)   During what months of the year is train spotting likely to be a cold and lonely hobby?
       (a)   January/February   (b)   March/April
       (c)   November/December   (d)   June/July

33)   What two seasons of the year make train spotting a pleasant hobby?
       (a)   Winter & Spring   (b)   Summer & Autumn
       (c)   Autumn & Winter   (d)   Spring & Summer

34) How long ago does it say that train spotting was a more interesting hobby?
    (a)   10 – 20 years ago   (b)   20 – 30 years ago
    (c)   30 – 40 years ago   (d)   40 – 50 years ago

35) What type of locomotives were the most common then?
    (a)   diesel   (b)   electric
    (c)   steam   (d)   petrol

36) During which decades were steam engines phased out?
    (a)   40's and 50's   (b)   50's and 60's
    (c)   60's and 70's   (d)   70's and 80's

37) What actually does a train spotter do?
    (a)   ride on different trains
    (b)   sit on station platforms all day long
    (c)   record the numbers of trains in a notebook
    (d)   wait for the 8.47 from London

In the passage below certain words are missing. The missing words are written out at the end of the passage. For each of the numbers 38 to 55 there is a word that fits in that space. Work out what that word is and mark your answers on the answer sheet provided.

There are very few people that do not like (38) . Right from a very early age we are introduced to the (39) of music. For example our mothers singing a (40) to get us to sleep when we were (41) , or the sounds of music coming from the radio or (42) in our houses. When we were at school, we would be taught about music and would sing songs and (43) in (44) . Those of us who were musically (45) would learn to play a musical (46) . At first this might be a recorder, then we would (47) to a (48), a guitar or perhaps a trumpet. As we got older we would begin to like (49) music in all its different forms, perhaps enjoying it so much that we would go to (50) to hear the music played in a (51) situation. Then as we come to the end of our (52), we would look back on our lives and associate a particular song or (53) with a (54)   (55) in our lives.

sounds   progress   event   lullaby   violin   television   assembly   inclined   days   instrument   babies   hymns   concerts   certain   live   music   tune   popular

CHECK THROUGH YOUR WORK FOR ANY MISTAKES OR OMISSIONS

PAPER 3

Read the passage below and then answer the questions that follow, which are based on the passage. It is about the nurse Florence Nightingale.

Florence Nightingale is remembered as the British nurse who tended the wounded soldiers of the Crimean War, but her life involved many influential acts. She was actually born in the town of Florence in Italy in 1820 whilst her parents were travelling around Europe. When they returned to England, Florence along with her sister, Parthenope, lived first at Lea Hurst in Derbyshire,
5 then at Embley in Hampshire.
When she was 17, Florence felt the voice of God calling her to do His work. In time she realised that this would be nursing, though at first her parents disapproved of this, as it was not considered proper for a woman of her background and education to do this. After travelling through Italy, Greece and Egypt, Florence settled in Germany where she spent three months learning about the
10 European system of nursing. On her return to Britain in 1853 she became the superintendent of the Hospital for Invalid Gentlewomen in Harley Street, London.
The following year she took thirty-eight female nurses with her to help out at the military hospitals in Turkey where the Crimean War was being fought. Apart from nursing the soldiers, Florence would write letters home from the invalid soldiers and established reading rooms in
15 the hospitals. In 1856 after the war was over, Florence Nightingale returned to Britain where she continued to make advances in nursing. In 1860 she set up the Nightingale Training School for Nurses at St Thomas' Hospital in London and also wrote the best selling *Notes On Nursing*, which is still used today by nurses the world over. In 1907 she became the first woman to receive the Order of Merit award and three years later after many years of
20 campaigning for improved standards in health care she died, aged 90.

1)   The meaning of "influential" (line 2) is: -
    (a)   Showing great bravery   (b)   Changing the way people think
    (c)   Acting in the correct manner   (d)   Writing to those with influence

2)   Florence Nightingale was born in: -
    (a) Egypt   (b) England   (c) Italy   (d) Greece

3)   "Disapproved" (line 7) means:
    (a) liked   (b) stopped   (c) weren't keen on   (d) allowed

4)   "Background" (line 8) means:
    (a) class   (b) schooling   (c) parents   (d) family

5)   Where did Florence learn all about European nursing?
    (a) Italy   (b) Greece   (c) Egypt   (d) Germany

6)   An "invalid" (line 11) is a person who: -
    (a)   Is disabled by illness or injury   (b)   Lives in a hospital
    (c)   Is training to be a nurse   (d)   Used to be a soldier

7)   "Military" (line 12) means: -
    (a)   Connected with nursing   (b)   Connected with Turkey
    (c)   Connected with reading   (d)   Connected with soldiers

8) Apart from nursing, how else did Florence help the soldiers?
(a) she played cards with them   (b) she taught them to read
(c) she wrote letters for them   (d) she read to them

9) Where did Florence set up her Nurses' Training School?
(a) Turkey   (b) Crimea   (c) London   (d) Germany

10) In what year did Florence Nightingale die?
(a) 1820   (b) 1860   (c) 1907   (d) 1910

Find a word from the group below which has the <u>same</u> meaning as the underlined word in each sentence and then mark your answer on the answer sheet.

breadth prompt hung exterior quantity calamity insolent omen ancient terror

11) The colourful light was <u>suspended</u> from the ceiling.

12) The customs officers seized a large <u>amount</u> of drugs.

13) The cheeky boy was very <u>rude</u> to the policeman.

14) When the ship sank it was a major <u>disaster</u>.

15) There was a lot of <u>fear</u> amongst those who had been caught in the storm.

16) The Aborigines saw the eclipse as the <u>sign</u> they were expecting.

17) The tourists enjoyed visiting the <u>old</u> monument.

18) A guard patrolled the <u>outside</u> of the factory.

19) We had to be <u>quick</u> getting back to the car.

20) The <u>width</u> of the swimming pool was ten metres.

Adjectives are words that describe nouns. In each line below find the adjective and mark your answer on the answer sheet provided.
An example has been done for you.

E.g.   The friendly giant picked up the boy from the ground.   *ANSWER: friendly*

21) We rushed to catch the departing train.

22) Samantha did very well in the tough game.

23) I like to watch comedy programmes on the television.

24) "Where on earth is this strange place?" said mum.

25) Michael fell over when he received a nasty tackle.

26) "Don't forget to do your Geography homework", said mum.

27) Rebecca didn't feel well after eating the chocolate cake.

28) Martin enjoyed seeing his best friend fall for the trick.

29) The large parcel was addressed to Steven.

30) "You are a very naughty girl!" said the teacher.

Read the passage below about a boy-king in ancient Egypt and then answer the questions on it. Mark your choice, a, b, c or d on the separate answer sheet.

In Karnak by the ancient River Nile, the sun had already risen high in the sky as the boy-king was woken by the royal servants. He felt tired, nervous and very hungry. This was the second day that he had not eaten, yet he knew that this fast was necessary so that he would be completely pure for the coronation ceremony that would take place later that day.

5 His chief servant gave him a cup filled with water. Eagerly he drank from it. Yet as soon as he finished, he felt a burning sensation in his throat. He comforted himself with the thought that within a few hours he would once again be able to eat – once the ceremonies had been completed. Then he would partake with all the most important people in Egypt in one gigantic feast that would last well into the night. He looked up and saw four priests entering his room. Of the four,

10 one carried a large urn, whilst another held a towel. The other two carried Holy Books above their heads. The leading priest came towards him and bowed.
"Oh Great Master, it is the hour of your purification. Please follow me".
The High Priest turned and walked over toward the altar situated at the far end of the room. The boy-king followed obediently, peaceful in the knowledge that the beginning of the end had come.

15 The High Priest bowed to the altar and placed the urn on the altar. He then turned to the boy-king who by now was kneeling obediently in front of him. He removed the lid from the urn and slowly raised it above the boy's head, distinctly saying the words,
"Oh Great Isis, Queen of our holy and noble land. Just as the Sacred Nile flows with life, so we ask You to impart the Holy and Royal life-giving Spirit into this your obedient servant Tutankhamun".

31) For how many days had the boy-king not eaten?
   (a) No days   (b) One day   (c) Two days   (d) Three days

32) What does "pure" mean (line 3)?
   (a) Tired   (b) Spotless   (c) Nervous   (d) Thirsty

33) What does "coronation ceremony" (line 4) refer to?
   (a) Being purified   (b) Fasting   (c) Feasting   (d) Being crowned king

34) What part of speech is "gigantic"? (line 8)
   (a) Adverb   (b) Noun   (c) Adjective   (d) Verb

35) What is an urn? (line 10)
   (a) A box   (b) A holy book   (c) A container   (d) A bowl

36) What word below best describes "altar"? (line 13)
   (a) A desk   (b) A chair   (c) A bed   (d) A table

37) "The beginning of the end had come" (line 14) means?
   (a) It wouldn't be long before the ceremony started   (b) The ceremony had ended
   (c) The final part was about to begin   (d) The whole event was almost over

38) "Obediently" (line 16) means?
   (a) Straightforward   (b) Confused   (c) Unsure   (d) Without arguing

39) "Sacred" (line 18) means?
    (a) Good   (b) Special   (c) Evil   (d) Fruitful

In the sentences below, choose one of the words in the brackets that fits in with the rest of the sentence. Mark your answers on the answer sheet. *An example has been done for you.*

E.g.   *The old lady had a home help who (arrested, assisted, agitated) her.*   *ANSWER: assisted*

40)   I was surprised by the variety of (fauna, fervour, flavour) in the forest.

41)   We were (adjunct, amazed, augmented) at the man's behaviour.

42)   You have (indebted, inherited, inscribed) a lot of money

43)   The high-wire artist showed great (angularity, astuteness, agility).

44)   Soldiers often (excelled, exhausted, exploited) ordinary people.

45)   The clever boy showed good (initiative, incense, ingest) in his work.

46)   My dentist said I had (plague, plaque, plage) on my teeth.

47)   Before me was a scene of utter (degradation, desolation, desperation).

In the sentences below, two words are in the wrong place. Work out what those words are, so that if they were swapped around, the sentence would make sense. Mark your answers on the separate answer sheet. *An example has been done for you.*

E.g.   *I tripped up on the paving leg and broke my stone.*   *ANSWER: leg stone*

48)   We were stuck in the time for a long queue.

49)   I wandered if me would like to come for a ride with you.

50)   "Where is the impatient painting?" asked the valuable tourist.

51)   The pocket child asked for some shy money.

52)   Take forty pounds from two pence and you will have one pound sixty.

53)   My heart started to beat faster the harder I ran.

54)   Steam engines rely on water to heat the coal to make steam.

55)   The important man missed his lazy appointment.

END OF TEST PAPER THREE

CHECK THROUGH YOUR PAPER TO SEE IF YOU HAVE MISSED ANY QUESTIONS OUT AND TO SEE IF YOU HAVE MADE ANY MISTAKES

PAPER 4

Read through the passage below and then answer the questions on it. Mark your choice, a, b, c or d on the answer sheet provided.

It was raining cats and dogs when Jackie came out of school.
"Look out!" shouted Katherine, her best friend, as the bus pulled up and sent a splash of rain water all over her dark blue school uniform. In the rush to get on the bus Jackie didn't have time to moan or complain. "Never mind", she thought. "It won't be long before I'm
5   seeing my heroes live on stage at Wembley". The thought seemed to give her some comfort. As soon as she got in, Jackie rushed upstairs and took a shower, leaving her wet school uniform littered about the landing.
"More haste, less speed!" shouted her mother, but Jackie couldn't hear a word her mother
10   said as she sang the latest hit by her boy band heroes.
Half an hour later, Jackie was in her dad's car, having picked up Katherine from her home a few streets away. Soon they were on the M25 speeding towards Wembley. Suddenly a line of red brake lights appeared on the horizon and Jackie's Dad braked gradually, before coming to a complete stop.
15   "It's pretty heavy tonight," said Dad. "Hopefully it will soon clear". Yet fifteen minutes later they had barely moved more than a few hundred metres. Time was running out and Jackie realized this. "Dad. Can't you do something! We've only got half an hour until show time. I couldn't bear missing seeing Gareth, Alex, Stu and Matt!" The whole evening was in jeopardy. Just then the wailing of an ambulance siren could be heard in the distance.
20   In no time at all it sped past them on the hard shoulder. Within another ten minutes they were on their way again. The show was due to start at 8 o'clock and they arrived with five minutes to spare. They all rushed round the corner to the entrance. There were just a few people about. Jackie thought most people must be inside now, but as they came to the entrance doors there was a large sign in front of them, which said, "Tonight's show – Cancelled"!!!!

1)   "It was raining cats and dogs" (line 1). Which word below describes this phrase?
    (a) Idiom   (b) Metaphor   (c) Conditional   (d) Tautology

2)   Another word for "moan" (line 4) would be: -
    (a) Cry   (b) Shout   (c) Disagree   (d) Groan

3)   What part of speech is "comfort" (line 6)?
    (a) Verb   (b) Adverb   (c) Noun   (d) Adjective

4)   "More haste less speed" (line 9) is a?
    (a) Colloquialism   (b) Parable   (c) Proverb   (d) Diminutive

5)   What do you think the "M25" is (line 12)?
    (a) A train   (b) A motorway   (c) A bridge   (d) A type of car

6)   Another word for "horizon" (line 13) would be?
    (a) Plane   (b) Distance   (c) Roadway   (d) Line

7) What part of speech is "complete" (line 14)?
   (a) Verb   (b) Adverb   (c) Noun   (d) Adjective

8) "Jeopardy" (line 18) means?
   (a) Collapse   (b) Safety   (c) Danger   (d) Serious

9) "Cancelled" (line 24) means?
   (a) Postponed   (b) Started   (c) Changed   (d) Stopped

Below is a list of different occupations. Look at the definition and work out which occupation matches the description. Mark your choice on the separate answer sheet.

carpenter / vet / butcher / glazier / accountant / chauffeur

navigator / chemist / gamekeeper / confectioner

10) This person drives important people to different places.

11) This person is concerned with the well being of animals.

12) This person looks after the money side of people's lives.

13) This person makes things out of wood.

14) This person is concerned with making up prescriptions.

15) This person provides meat for people.

16) This person repairs and replaces windows.

17) This person will guide a ship or plane on a journey.

18) This person makes cakes and pastries.

19) This person protects animals from poachers.

Verbs are doing words or words of action. Find the <u>two verbs</u> **in each sentence and mark your answers on the answer sheet.** *An example has been done for you.*

E.g.   *The children ran down the hill to catch the ball.*   *ANSWER: ran catch*

20) We jumped off the ledge when the guard-dog approached us.

21) I like to watch cricket matches in the summer.

22) The spacemen travelled to the Planet Jupiter to start a new colony there.

23) James slipped on the wet stone as he ran across the stream

24) "Which bus goes to the city centre?" I asked the bus driver.

25) The boy had soon opened his model kit and completed the model.

26) My mother made some jam with the strawberries she picked.

27) I didn't know how to do this sum.

28) The hairdresser tried to cut my hair.

29) When I reach the age of eighteen, I will leave home.

Below is a recipe for making a cake. Read through the passage and then answer the questions below, marking your answers on the separate answer sheet.

Recipe for a Victoria Sandwich Cake

Ingredients:-   100 g / 4oz butter or margarine   100 g / 4oz sugar
                        100 g / 4oz self-raising flour   2 large eggs
                        ($\frac{1}{4}$ teaspoon of vanilla essence)   Strawberry or raspberry jam & icing sugar

Lightly grease two sandwich tins (approx. 15cm diameter) and   line each base with greaseproof paper. Mix the butter/margarine with the sugar in a large bowl, (either by hand or with an electric mixer), until the mixture is light and airy. Gently mix in the eggs and then add the vanilla essence if this is wanted. When all this has been mixed in, start adding the flour
5   through the sieve, folding it gradually into the mixture. Put the mixture equally into the two tins and then bake in the oven at Gas Mark 4 (180°C) for about 25 minutes. The cakes should be golden brown and have raised themselves up. Take them out of the oven and leave them to cool for a few minutes, before putting them out onto a wire stand to cool completely. Once the two   cakes have cooled spread some jam over one and then   put the two cakes together.
10   Finally, mix some icing sugar with a little water to make a paste which can then be spread over the top of the cake.

30)   Why do you think the ingredients mention both butter or margarine ?
    (a)   The person who wrote the recipe isn't sure which one to use
    (b)   So people can make their own choice as to which one to use
    (c)   It is a mistake by the person typing the ingredients
    (d)   To confuse the reader

31)   Why do you think the ingredient vanilla essence is in brackets?
    (a)   It is a mistake made by the person typing the ingredients
    (b)   The author is not sure if it should be in this recipe
    (c)   Some cooks don't like to include it in their cakes
    (d)   To confuse the reader

32)   Why do the last two ingredients not have any amount put next to them?
    (a)   The author has forgotten to put them in
    (b)   It is up to the person making the cake to decide how much of them to use
    (c)   They might not be needed and so no amounts are included
    (d)   The person typing the ingredients list forgot to put them in

33)   "Approx." (line 1) means: -
    (a) exactly   (b) measuring   (c) roughly   (d) in metric terms

34)   In what condition should the mixture be before the eggs are added?
    (a) light/airy   (b) light/fluffy   (c) smooth/airy   (d) smooth/fluffy

35)   How many eggs are added at this stage?
    (a) None   (b) One   (c) Two   (d) Three

36)   What utensil is used to add the flour to the mixture?
    (a) A spoon   (b) A sieve   (c) A whisk   (d) A knife

37) What does "equally" (line 5) mean?
    (a) different proportions   (b) large amounts
    (c) small amounts   (d) The same amounts

38) At what temperature should the cakes be cooked in the oven?
    (a) 100°C   (b) 150°C   (c) 160°C   (d) 180°C

39) What is put into the middle of the two cakes?
    (a) sauce   (b) sugar   (c) jam   (d) eggs

In each line below find the <u>opposite</u> of the word underlined, using one of the words in italics. Mark your answers on the answer sheet.

few   drunk   poverty   noise   cheap   hero   success   cramped   moving   plentiful

40) The <u>sober</u> man woke up on the park bench.
41) I enjoyed the peace and <u>quiet</u> of the countryside.
42) The <u>coward</u> managed to run after the bank robber.
43) The <u>stationary</u> vehicle eventually stopped.
44) There were <u>numerous</u> insects crawling in the shed.
45) This year we had a <u>barren</u> harvest.
46) My father wished the newly wed couple <u>prosperity.</u>
47) Our house is very <u>spacious</u> with plenty of room.
48) His business venture was a <u>failure.</u>
49) The champagne was ever so <u>expensive.</u>

In the sentences below one of the words has been spelt incorrectly. Identify that word and then mark your answer on the answer sheet
An example has been done for you.

E.g.   *"Wear are you going?" asked the policeman*   *ANSWER: Wear*

50) It was a very quite night as the snow began to fall.
51) The boys team one the league cup once again.
52) My father tolled me off for interrupting his sleep.
53) The shop had a wide variety of stationary.
54) I wasn't sure if I was aloud to watch the TV programme.
55) The robber used course language when he was arrested.
56) Their wasn't anyone to take in the abandoned dog.
57) We rushed passed the school gate at the end of school.
58) I had to practice my times tables every day.
59) The guilty man frose on the spot as the police arrived.
60) My dad had to break suddenly in his car yesterday.

END OF TEST PAPER FOUR

Notes For Parents

About the A Plus Series of Secondary School Entrance 11+ Practice Papers

The A Plus Series of Secondary School entrance practice papers have been designed to help children familiarise themselves with the wide variety of questions that are set in secondary school entrance examinations at age 11 or 12 for both state or private schools. Approximately twenty different types of English questions are covered in the two volumes so that your child will gain a wide experience of the types of questions that are usually set in these examinations. The questions are designed to be easier at first and then get harder as you go on, so that your child will not become disheartened. The practice papers are also designed to give your child the chance to work quickly and efficiently under timed conditions. The questions in Volume One are designed to be completed before Volume Two so that your child's understanding and confidence can be built up over the two volumes. With this set of English practice papers, the answers are set out in **multiple choice format.**

How to administer the practice papers

When your child sits these papers it is best to find a quiet place in the house where he or she will not be disturbed. It is also best to sit these papers at a time of day when your child is most mentally alert - usually in the morning after breakfast if at all possible.

This set of English practice papers contains separate answers sheets for your child to mark his/her answers on. Please cut/detach these from the back of this booklet. All your child has to do is to draw a short horizontal line in pencil across a small rectangular box (with a ruler if they wish). There is a choice of four or five possible answers for most questions, so your child needs to work out which answer s/he will choose from the question paper first of all. Most of the questions ask for just one answer, though there are some which require two answers. If s/he wants to change an answer, all s/he has to do is rub out the line and mark a new line in another box.

The timing of the tests is also equally important. Your child should be given 45 minutes to complete each English paper. It may be quite possible that for the first few tests your child will not have enough time to complete the whole test. This is understandable, as children need to learn to pace themselves, as well as become used to answering the different types of questions. If your child does not complete a paper, make a mark on the paper to show how far s/he has reached in 45 minutes, and then let him/her finish the rest of the questions in his/her own time. A good idea is to say when 20 minutes have passed and when there are 5 minutes to go. It is also important to emphasise that if your child finds that they cannot answer a question, they should put a mark in the margin of the question paper and not waste any more time attempting the question. Instead, if there is any time left, once they have finished the test, they should come back to that question. They are allowed to use any spare space on the question paper for working out their answers. When marking the paper, there is always one mark for each correct answer, even if there are two parts to a particular question. The answers to the questions can be found on the next two pages.

Text © Mark Chatterton 1996/2006
English (Multiple Choice Format) Volume One   9781901146578
Published by: Hadleigh Books, Church Road, Hadleigh, Essex, SS7 2HA
Printed by: CPI Antony Rowe Ltd, 48-50 Birch Close, Eastbourne, East Sussex, BN23 6PE

PUPIL ANSWER SHEET FOR PAPER 1

PLEASE MARK YOUR ANSWERS IN PENCIL ONLY. DRAW A STRAIGHT LINE ACROSS THE BOX
NEXT TO THE ANSWER THAT YOU CHOOSE. IF YOU WISH TO CHANGE AN ANSWER RUB IT OUT
AND PUT A FRESH LINE IN A DIFFERENT SPACE. THERE IS AN EXAMPLE TO HELP YOU

1) A □ B □ C □ D □   2) A □ B □ C □ D □   3) A □ B □ C □ D □   4) A □ B □ C □ D □   5) A □ B □ C □ D □   6) A □ B □ C □ D □   7) A □ B □ C □ D □

8) A □ B □ C □ D □   Eg) ? □ ! □ " " ■ . □   9) ? □ ! □ " " □ . □   10) ? □ ! □ " " □ . □   11) ? □ ! □ " " □ . □   12) ? □ ! □ " " □ . □

13) ? □ ! □ " " □ . □   14) ? □ ! □ " " □ . □   15) ? □ ! □ " " □ . □   16) ? □ ! □ " " □ . □   17) ? □ ! □ " " □ . □   18) ? □ ! □ " " □ . □

19) ible □ able □   20) ible □ able □   21) ible □ able □   22) ible □ able □   23) ible □ able □

24) ible □ able □   25) ible □ able □   26) ible □ able □   27) ible □ able □   28) ible □ able □

29) A □ B □ C □ D □   30) A □ B □ C □ D □   31) A □ B □ C □ D □   32) A □ B □ C □ D □   33) A □ B □ C □ D □   34) A □ B □ C □ D □   35) A □ B □ C □ D □

36)
water □
warden □
walrus □
wander □
waist □

37)
mathematics □
marriage □
manor □
major □
mayor □

38)
injure □
institute □
injustice □
indeed □
injury □

39)
yearn □
yacht □
yarn □
young □
yesterday □

40)
office □
offend □
offence □
official □
offer □

41)
article □
arthritis □
armoury □
argument □
articulate □

42)
particle □
pardon □
particular □
party □
parliament □

43)
hotel □
holiday □
hospital □
holdall □
hostess □

44)
creative □
crying □
creation □
cradle □
creamery □

45)
united □
university □
uniform □
unity □
unicorn □

46)
sew □
sow □

47)
oar □
ore □

48)
threw □
through □

49)
fowl □
foul □

50)
There □
their □

51)
bored □
board □

52)
beach □
beech □

53)
current □
currant □

54)
wear □
where □

55)
made □
maid □

END OF THE PUPIL ANSWER SHEET FOR PAPER ONE

PUPIL ANSWER SHEET FOR PAPER 2

PLEASE MARK YOUR ANSWERS IN PENCIL ONLY. DRAW A STRAIGHT LINE ACROSS THE BOX
NEXT TO THE ANSWER THAT YOU CHOOSE. IF YOU WISH TO CHANGE AN ANSWER RUB IT OUT
AND PUT A FRESH LINE IN A DIFFERENT SPACE. THERE IS AN EXAMPLE TO HELP YOU

1) A ☐ B ☐ C ☐ D ☐
2) A ☐ B ☐ C ☐ D ☐
3) A ☐ B ☐ C ☐ D ☐
4) A ☐ B ☐ C ☐ D ☐
5) A ☐ B ☐ C ☐ D ☐
6) A ☐ B ☐ C ☐ D ☐
7) A ☐ B ☐ C ☐ D ☐

Eg
- We'el ☐
- We'l ☐
- We'll ■
- We'ul ☐
- Wel'l ☐

8)
- you'wl ☐
- you'l ☐
- yo'll ☐
- you'll ☐
- you'ul ☐

9)
- doo'nt ☐
- don'ot ☐
- d'not ☐
- do'ot ☐
- don't ☐

10)
- must'ot ☐
- mustn't ☐
- mu'nt ☐
- mus'nt ☐
- must'nt ☐

11)
- heh'd ☐
- he'ad ☐
- he'd ☐
- heha' ☐
- he'ed ☐

12)
- must've ☐
- must'ave ☐
- must'e ☐
- must'ov ☐
- must'av ☐

13)
- cann't ☐
- can'ot ☐
- can't ☐
- cano't ☐
- can'nt ☐

14)
- shoul'nt ☐
- should'n ☐
- should't ☐
- shouldn't ☐
- should'ot ☐

15)
- I'hd ☐
- I'ad ☐
- I'd ☐
- ih'd ☐
- I'ha ☐

16)
- could't ☐
- couldnt' ☐
- couldn't ☐
- could'nt ☐
- could'n ☐

17)
- you'ar ☐
- you're ☐
- you'e ☐
- youa'e ☐
- youar' ☐

18)
- fell ☐
- off ☐
- ladder ☐
- broke ☐
- ankle ☐

19)
- shut ☐
- door ☐
- before ☐
- leave ☐
- room ☐

20)
- Liverpool ☐
- beat ☐
- Chelsea ☐
- 4 ☐
- 1 ☐

21)
- old ☐
- man ☐
- very ☐
- nasty ☐
- cough ☐

22)
- last ☐
- week ☐
- could ☐
- leave ☐
- house ☐

23)
- raging ☐
- river ☐
- moving ☐
- huge ☐
- boulders ☐

24)
- every ☐
- day ☐
- hope ☐
- weather ☐
- sunny ☐

25)
- why ☐
- visit ☐
- old ☐
- castle ☐
- Dad ☐

26)
- each ☐
- morning ☐
- loud ☐
- banging ☐
- heard ☐

27)
- where ☐
- the ☐
- airport ☐
- asked ☐
- visitor ☐

28) A ☐ B ☐ C ☐ D ☐
29) A ☐ B ☐ C ☐ D ☐
30) A ☐ B ☐ C ☐ D ☐
31) A ☐ B ☐ C ☐ D ☐
32) A ☐ B ☐ C ☐ D ☐
33) A ☐ B ☐ C ☐ D ☐
34) A ☐ B ☐ C ☐ D ☐

35) A ☐ B ☐ C ☐ D ☐
36) A ☐ B ☐ C ☐ D ☐
37) A ☐ B ☐ C ☐ D ☐

38)
- sounds ☐
- music ☐
- television ☐

39)
- sounds ☐
- days ☐
- hymns ☐

40)
- tune ☐
- hymns ☐
- lullaby ☐

41)
- days ☐
- babies ☐
- popular ☐

42)
- violin ☐
- music ☐
- television ☐

43)
- hymns ☐
- music ☐
- babies ☐

44)
- tune ☐
- assembly ☐
- television ☐

45)
- popular ☐
- inclined ☐
- live ☐

46)
- violin ☐
- event ☐
- instrument ☐

47)
- inclined ☐
- live ☐
- progress ☐

48)
- violin ☐
- tune ☐
- television ☐

49)
- sounds ☐
- television ☐
- popular ☐

50)
- sounds ☐
- concerts ☐
- assembly ☐

51)
- live ☐
- music ☐
- popular ☐

52)
- days ☐
- progress ☐
- sounds ☐

53)
- music ☐
- instrument ☐
- tune ☐

54)
- popular ☐
- certain ☐
- tune ☐

55)
- sounds ☐
- event ☐
- lullaby ☐

END OF THE PUPIL ANSWER SHEET FOR PAPER TWO

PUPIL ANSWER SHEET FOR PAPER 3

PLEASE MARK YOUR ANSWERS IN PENCIL ONLY. DRAW A STRAIGHT LINE ACROSS THE BOX NEXT TO THE ANSWER THAT YOU CHOOSE. IF YOU WISH TO CHANGE AN ANSWER RUB IT OUT AND PUT A FRESH LINE IN A DIFFERENT SPACE. THERE IS AN EXAMPLE TO HELP YOU.

1) A ☐ B ☐ C ☐ D ☐
2) A ☐ B ☐ C ☐ D ☐
3) A ☐ B ☐ C ☐ D ☐
4) A ☐ B ☐ C ☐ D ☐
5) A ☐ B ☐ C ☐ D ☐
6) A ☐ B ☐ C ☐ D ☐
7) A ☐ B ☐ C ☐ D ☐

8) A ☐ B ☐ C ☐ D ☐
9) A ☐ B ☐ C ☐ D ☐
10) A ☐ B ☐ C ☐ D ☐

11) prompt ☐ hung ☐ quantity ☐
12) calamity ☐ prompt ☐ quantity ☐
13) prompt ☐ insolent ☐ terror ☐

14) exterior ☐ calamity ☐ quantity ☐
15) prompt ☐ insolent ☐ terror ☐
16) calamity ☐ hung ☐ omen ☐
17) ancient ☐ calamity ☐ exterior ☐
18) quantity ☐ exterior ☐ calamity ☐

19) prompt ☐ hung ☐ breadth ☐
20) omen ☐ breadth ☐ prompt ☐
21) rushed ☐ catch ☐ departing ☐ train ☐
22) did ☐ well ☐ tough ☐ game ☐
23) like ☐ watch ☐ comedy ☐ television ☐

24) Where ☐ earth ☐ strange ☐ place ☐
25) over ☐ received ☐ nasty ☐ tackle ☐
26) forget ☐ geography ☐ homework ☐ mum ☐
27) feel ☐ well ☐ chocolate ☐ cake ☐
28) enjoyed ☐ seeing ☐ best ☐ trick ☐

29) large ☐ parcel ☐ addressed ☐ Steven ☐
30) are ☐ naughty ☐ girl ☐ teacher ☐
31) A ☐ B ☐ C ☐ D ☐
32) A ☐ B ☐ C ☐ D ☐
33) A ☐ B ☐ C ☐ D ☐

34) A ☐ B ☐ C ☐ D ☐
35) A ☐ B ☐ C ☐ D ☐
36) A ☐ B ☐ C ☐ D ☐
37) A ☐ B ☐ C ☐ D ☐
38) A ☐ B ☐ C ☐ D ☐
39) A ☐ B ☐ C ☐ D ☐

40) fauna ☐ fervour ☐ flavour ☐
41) adjunct ☐ amazed ☐ augmented ☐
42) indebted ☐ inherited ☐ inscribed ☐
43) angularity ☐ astuteness ☐ agility ☐

44) excelled ☐ exhausted ☐ exploited ☐
45) initiative ☐ incense ☐ ingest ☐
46) plague ☐ plaque ☐ plage ☐
47) degradation ☐ desolation ☐ desperation ☐

Eg) tripped ☐ paving ☐ leg ■ broke ☐ stone ■
48) were ☐ stuck ☐ time ☐ long ☐ queue ☐
49) me ☐ would ☐ like ☐ ride ☐ you ☐
50) where ☐ impatient ☐ painting ☐ valuable ☐ tourist ☐
51) pocket ☐ child ☐ asked ☐ shy ☐ money ☐

52) forty ☐ pounds ☐ two ☐ pence ☐ sixty ☐
53) heart ☐ started ☐ beat ☐ harder ☐ faster ☐
54) steam ☐ engines ☐ water ☐ heat ☐ coal ☐
55) important ☐ man ☐ missed ☐ lazy ☐ appointment ☐

END OF THE PUPIL ANSWER SHEET FOR PAPER THREE

PUPIL ANSWER SHEET FOR PAPER 4

PLEASE MARK YOUR ANSWERS IN PENCIL ONLY. DRAW A STRAIGHT LINE ACROSS THE BOX NEXT TO THE ANSWER THAT YOU CHOOSE. IF YOU WISH TO CHANGE AN ANSWER RUB IT OUT AND PUT A FRESH LINE IN A DIFFERENT SPACE. THERE ARE EXAMPLES TO HELP YOU.

1) A ☐ B ☐ C ☐ D ☐
2) A ☐ B ☐ C ☐ D ☐
3) A ☐ B ☐ C ☐ D ☐
4) A ☐ B ☐ C ☐ D ☐
5) A ☐ B ☐ C ☐ D ☐
6) A ☐ B ☐ C ☐ D ☐
7) A ☐ B ☐ C ☐ D ☐

8) A ☐ B ☐ C ☐ D ☐
9) A ☐ B ☐ C ☐ D ☐

10) glazier ☐ navigator ☐ chauffeur ☐
11) carpenter ☐ vet ☐ butcher ☐
12) glazier ☐ accountant ☐ chemist ☐

13) carpenter ☐ butcher ☐ chemist ☐
14) glazier ☐ accountant ☐ chemist ☐
15) chemist ☐ vet ☐ butcher ☐
16) glazier ☐ navigator ☐ chauffeur ☐
17) glazier ☐ navigator ☐ chauffeur ☐

Eg ran ■ down ☐ hill ☐ catch ■
20) jumped ☐ ledge ☐ guard-dog ☐ approached ☐
21) like ☐ watch ☐ cricket ☐ summer ☐

18) chauffeur ☐ confectioner ☐ gamekeeper ☐
19) chauffeur ☐ confectioner ☐ gamekeeper ☐

22) spacemen ☐ travelled ☐ start ☐ colony ☐
23) slipped ☐ wet ☐ ran ☐ stream ☐
24) which ☐ goes ☐ city ☐ asked ☐
25) soon ☐ opened ☐ completed ☐ model ☐
26) mother ☐ made ☐ jam ☐ picked ☐

27) know ☐ how ☐ do ☐ sum ☐
28) hairdresser ☐ tried ☐ cut ☐ hair ☐
29) when ☐ reach ☐ leave ☐ home ☐
30) A ☐ B ☐ C ☐ D ☐
31) A ☐ B ☐ C ☐ D ☐
32) A ☐ B ☐ C ☐ D ☐

33) A ☐ B ☐ C ☐ D ☐
34) A ☐ B ☐ C ☐ D ☐
35) A ☐ B ☐ C ☐ D ☐
36) A ☐ B ☐ C ☐ D ☐
37) A ☐ B ☐ C ☐ D ☐
38) A ☐ B ☐ C ☐ D ☐
39) A ☐ B ☐ C ☐ D ☐

40) drunk ☐ hero ☐ cheap ☐
41) poverty ☐ noise ☐ success ☐
42) drunk ☐ noise ☐ hero ☐
43) noise ☐ moving ☐ success ☐
44) few ☐ moving ☐ plentiful ☐

45) cramped ☐ moving ☐ plentiful ☐
46) poverty ☐ success ☐ noise ☐
47) cheap ☐ plentiful ☐ cramped ☐
48) success ☐ drunk ☐ plentiful ☐
49) drunk ☐ hero ☐ cheap ☐

Eg Wear ■ going ☐ asked ☐ policeman ☐
50) very ☐ quite ☐ night ☐ began ☐
51) team ☐ one ☐ league ☐ again ☐
52) father ☐ tolled ☐ interrupting ☐ sleep ☐
53) shop ☐ wide ☐ variety ☐ stationary ☐

54) wasn't ☐ sure ☐ aloud ☐ programme ☐
55) robber ☐ course ☐ language ☐ arrested ☐
56) their ☐ wasn't ☐ anyone ☐ abandoned ☐
57) rushed ☐ passed ☐ school ☐ gate ☐
58) practice ☐ times ☐ tables ☐ every ☐

59) guilty ☐ frose ☐ heard ☐ name ☐
60) break ☐ suddenly ☐ car ☐ yesterday ☐

END OF THE PUPIL ANSWER SHEET FOR PAPER FOUR

ANSWERS: ENGLISH VOLUME 1 PAPER ONE (MC)

1)	c	16)	?	31)	d	46)	sew
2)	b	17)	!	32)	a	47)	ore
3)	b	18)	""	33)	b	48)	threw
4)	d	19)	ible	34)	a	49)	fowl
5)	d	20)	able	35)	b	50)	their
6)	c	21)	ible	36)	wander	51)	bored
7)	b	22)	ible	37)	marriage	52)	beech
8)	a	23)	able	38)	injury	53)	currant
9)	.	24)	able	39)	yearn	54)	where
10)	!	25)	able	40)	offer	55)	made
11)	?	26)	ible	41)	arthritis		
12)	.	27)	able	42)	particle		
13)	""	28)	ible	43)	hospital		
14)	""	29)	b	44)	creation		
15)	.	30)	c	45)	united		

ANSWERS: ENGLISH VOLUME 1 PAPER TWO (MC)

1)	d	16)	Couldn't	31)	a	46)	instrument
2)	c	17)	You're	32)	c	47)	progress
3)	d	18)	ladder ankle	33)	d	48)	violin
4)	a	19)	door room	34)	c	49)	popular
5)	c	20)	Liverpool Chelsea	35)	c	50)	concerts
6)	b	21)	man cough	36)	b	51)	live
7)	a	22)	week house	37)	c	52)	days
8)	you'll	23)	river boulders	38)	music	53)	tune
9)	don't	24)	day weather	39)	sounds	54)	certain
10)	mustn't	25)	castle dad	40)	lullaby	55)	event
11)	he'd	26)	morning banging	41)	babies		
12)	must've	27)	airport visitor	42)	television		
13)	can't	28)	b	43)	hymns		
14)	shouldn't	29)	d	44)	assembly		
15)	I'd	30)	c	45)	inclined		

ANSWERS: ENGLISH VOLUME 1 PAPER THREE (MC)

1)	b	16)	omen	31)	c	46)	plaque
2)	c	17)	ancient	32)	b	47)	desolation
3)	c	18)	exterior	33)	d	48)	time queue
4)	a	19)	prompt	34)	c	49)	me you
5)	d	20)	breadth	35)	c	50)	impatient
6)	a	21)	departing	36)	d		valuable
7)	d	22)	tough	37)	c	51)	pocket shy
8)	c	23)	comedy	38)	d	52)	pounds pence
9)	c	24)	strange	39)	b	53)	harder faster
10)	d	25)	nasty	40)	fauna	54)	water coal
11)	hung	26)	Geography	41)	amazed	55)	important
12)	quantity	27)	chocolate	42)	inherited		lazy
13)	insolent	28)	best	43)	agility		
14)	calamity	29)	large	44)	exploited		
15)	terror	30)	naughty	45)	initiative		

ANSWERS: ENGLISH VOLUME 1 PAPER FOUR (MC)

1)	a	16)	glazier	31)	c	46)	poverty
2)	d	17)	navigator	32)	b	47)	cramped
3)	c	18)	confectioner	33)	c	48)	success
4)	c	19)	gamekeeper	34)	a	49)	cheap
5)	b	20)	jumped approached	35)	b	50)	quite
6)	b	21)	like watch	36)	b	51)	one
7)	d	22)	travelled start	37)	d	52)	tolled
8)	c	23)	slipped ran	38)	d	53)	stationary
9)	d	24)	goes asked	39)	c	54)	aloud
10)	chauffeur	25)	opened completed	40)	drunk	55)	course
11)	vet	26)	made picked	41)	noise	56)	Their
12)	accountant	27)	know do	42)	hero	57)	passed
13)	carpenter	28)	tried cut	43)	moving	58)	practice
14)	chemist	29)	reach leave	44)	few	59)	frose
15)	butcher	30)	b	45)	plentiful	60)	break